DRAUPADI

DRUPADA, KING OF PANCHALA, WAS PERFORMING A GRAND YAGNA, TO OBTAIN A MIGHTY SON.

AS THE FLAMES OF THE SACRIFICIAL FIRE LEAPT HIGH—

MAY AN EXCELLENT SON EMERGE FROM THIS FIRE!

AND FORTHWITH FROM THE FIRE SPRANG A YOUTH, HANDSOME, STRONG AND ARMOUR-CLAD.

LET THE BOY BE CALLED DHRISHTA-DYUMNA.

THEN TO THE AMAZEMENT OF ALL, THERE AROSE FROM THE SAME FIRE A DARK MAIDEN, TOO, WAFTING THE FRAGRANCE OF THE BLUE LOTUS IN BLOOM.

THIS GIRL IS AN EXCEPTIONAL WOMAN. SHE WILL BRING ABOUT THE DESTRUCTION OF THE KAURAVAS.

THE BRAHMANS CHOSE A NAME FOR HER.

DARK AND BEAUTIFUL AS SHE IS, LET HER BE NAMED KRISHNAA.

AS THE DAUGHTER OF DRUPADA SHE SHALL BE CALLED DRAUPADI.

FROM THE MOMENT HE RECEIVED THE UNEXPECTED CELESTIAL GIFT OF THIS UNMATCHED GIRL AS HIS DAUGHTER, ONE THOUGHT OBSESSED DRUPADA—HER MARRIAGE.

ARJUNA, THE VALIANT PANDAVA WOULD HAVE BEEN AN IDEAL HUSBAND FOR MY DAUGHTER. IF ONLY HE, HIS MOTHER, AND BROTHERS HAD SURVIVED THAT FATEFUL FIRE AT VARANA-VATA.

AS THE PRINCES LISTENED TO HIS STORY, KUNTI WATCHING THEIR FACES GUESSED THE STATE OF HER SONS' MINDS.

EACH ONE OF THEM SEEMS TO BE KEEN ON WINNING THE CHASTE DRAUPADI AT THAT SWAYAMVARA.

LATER SHE CALLED THEM TO HER.

LET US PROCEED TO THE KINGDOM OF PANCHALA. DRUPADA'S CHARITY TO BRAHMANS KNOWS NO BOUNDS.

WHAT DO MY BROTHERS SAY?

LET US GO!

THEY SET FORTH FOR PANCHALA. ON THE WAY THEY MET SAGE VYASA. WHEN THEY TOLD HIM WHERE THEY WERE GOING –

COME, LET ME TELL YOU OF AN EARLIER BIRTH OF DRAUPADI WHEN SHE WAS THE DAUGHTER OF A RISHI.

"THOUGH BEAUTIFUL, CHASTE AND ACCOMPLISHED SHE WAS FATED TO REMAIN UNMARRIED."

WITH SEVERE PENANCES TO LORD SHIVA SHALL I TRIUMPH OVER MY FATE.

"YEARS OF PENANCE BROUGHT THEIR REWARD. SHIVA APPEARED BEFORE HER."

WHAT FAVOUR DO YOU SEEK FROM ME?

"IN UNCONTROLLED EAGERNESS THE GIRL REPEATED HER REQUEST FIVE TIMES."

AN ACCOMPLISHED HUSBAND...AN ACCOMPLISHED HUSBAND...AN...

"SHIVA SMILED"

SO BE IT. YOU SHALL HAVE FIVE HUSBANDS FROM AMONG THE BHARATA PRINCES.

"THE GIRL WAS CONFOUNDED."

LORD! I...I...IT WAS ONLY ONE HUSBAND THAT I WANTED.

"SHIVA'S WORDS ONCE UTTERED COULD NOT BE REVOKED. BUT--"

THE EVENT CAN BE POSTPONED. YOU WILL HAVE THE FIVE HUSBANDS IN ANOTHER LIFE.

YOU, THE FIVE PANDAVAS, ARE THE FIVE HUSBANDS DRAUPADI IS DESTINED TO HAVE. DESTINY AWAITS YOU IN PANCHALA. MAKE HER YOURS.

AND VYASA WENT HIS WAY.

FULL OF HOPE, THE PRINCES AND THEIR MOTHER PROCEEDED TO PANCHALA.

THE CAPITAL CITY OF PANCHALA WAS HUMMING WITH EXCITEMENT.

THEY SAY THAT DURYODHANA AND THE KAURAVAS WITH SHAKUNI, THEIR UNCLE, AND KARNA THEIR FRIEND, ARE HERE.

KUNTI AND HER SONS CHOSE A POTTER'S HOUSE TO LIVE IN. AFTER RESTING FOR SOME TIME—

LET US GO TO THE SWAYAMVARA AND TAKE OUR PLACE AMONG THE BRAHMANS.

6

THE GREAT DAY DAWNED. WHEN ALL WERE ASSEMBLED, DHRISHTADYUMNA CAME FORWARD LEADING DRAUPADI.

HEAR O KINGS! THIS IS THE BOW. THE NOBLEMAN WHO HITS THE MARK SHALL TODAY WED MY SISTER.

KARNA WAS AMONG THE FIRST TO TRY. THE PANDAVAS WERE DISMAYED.

IT'S KARNA! WE MAY CONSIDER THE MARK AS ALREADY HIT.

BUT AS KARNA STRUNG THE BOW AND TOOK AIM —

I WILL NEVER MARRY ONE OF THE * SUTA CASTE!

YOU SHOULD NOT HAVE HUMILIATED ME SO, DRAUPADI.

*SUTA = AN INFERIOR KSHATRIYA.

7

ONE BY ONE THE OTHERS TRIED AND FAILED. WHEN ALL OF THEM HAD GIVEN UP, ARJUNA STEPPED FORWARD.

A HUMBLE BRAHMAN. YET HOW NOBLE AND CONFIDENT IS HIS BEARING.

ARJUNA'S ARROW FOUND ITS MARK.

HE HAS SUCCEEDED!!

FULL OF JOY, DRAUPADI CAME UP TO ARJUNA WITH A GARLAND OF FLOWERS.

MEANWHILE KUNTI WAS WORRIED.

MY SONS ARE LATE. HAVE THEIR COUSINS RECOGNIZED THEM AND KILLED THEM? WAS VYASA MISTAKEN IN...

SUDDENLY—

LOOK MOTHER! SEE WHAT WE HAVE BROUGHT TODAY!

WHATEVER IT IS, SHARE IT EQUALLY AND ENJOY IT.

A MOMENT LATER SHE CAME OUT AND SAW DRAUPADI.

ALAS! YUDHISHTHIRA, WHAT HAVE I SAID!

ARJUNA WON HER. IT IS PROPER THAT HE MARRY HER.

AND COMMIT THE SIN OF IGNORING MY MOTHER'S ORDERS?

NO YUDHISHTHIRA, WE SHALL EACH ONE OF US MARRY HER. YOU THE ELDEST FIRST, THEN BHEEMA, THEN MYSELF AND THEN THE TWINS.

ALL RIGHT! THEN DRAUPADI SHALL BE A WIFE TO ALL OF US.

BY THEN DURYODHANA HAD LEARNT THAT IT WAS THE PANDAVAS WHO HAD WON DRAUPADI. BACK AT HASTINAPURA HE WENT TO HIS FATHER, THE BLIND DHRITHARASHTRA.

ALAS! THE PANDAVAS HAVE ESCAPED. AND THEY HAVE THE MIGHTY DRUPADA AND HIS SON AS ALLIES.

O KING! LET US ATTACK DRUPADA AND CAPTURE THE PANDAVAS.

BUT THE KURU ELDERS ADVISED DHRITHARASHTRA AGAINST THIS.

IF YOU WANT TO BE JUST, SEND FOR THE PANDAVAS AND GIVE THEM HALF THE KINGDOM.

GO THEN, VIDURA. BRING THEM BACK.

WHEN THE PANDAVAS RETURNED TO HASTINAPURA—

THE HEROIC SONS OF PANDU ARE ALIVE!

THE VIRTUOUS ONES HAVE AGREED TO RETURN TO THE CITY.

WE ARE BLESSED!

WHEN THEY CAME TO PAY THEIR RESPECTS TO DHRITHARASHTRA—

I GRANT YOU HALF THE KINGDOM. GO TO KHANDAVAPRASTHA AND RULE FROM THERE. MAY ALL PROSPERITY BE YOURS.

WE SHALL DO AS YOU SAY.

HAVING OBTAINED THEIR RIGHTFUL SHARE OF THE KINGDOM THE EVER-TRUTHFUL YUDHISHTHIRA AND HIS BROTHERS RULED VIRTUOUSLY OVER IT.

DURYODHANA, MORE ENVIOUS THAN EVER, PLOTTED WITH HIS UNCLE SHAKUNI.

O UNCLE, IS THERE NO WAY TO RUIN MY COUSINS?

THERE IS. BY A GAME OF DICE. YUDHISHTHIRA IS AN ADDICT AND I AM SHARP. WE WILL WIN.

WHEN THE INVITATION TO PLAY REACHED YUDHISHTHIRA—

I AM UNWILLING TO GAMBLE WITH SHAKUNI WHO, IT IS KNOWN, CHEATS AT DICE. BUT I MUST ACCEPT THE ROYAL CHALLENGE.

AT THE GAME YUDHISHTHIRA STAKED ALL HIS WEALTH, THEN HIS BROTHERS AND THEN HIMSELF, AND LOST ALL.

O KING, THERE IS STILL ONE DEAR STAKE YOU HOLD ON TO — DRAUPADI. STAKE HER AND WIN YOURSELF BACK.

SHAME! SHAME!

YUDHISHTHIRA HAD TO AGREE. SHAKUNI CAST THE DICE.

LOOK! I WIN AGAIN.

ALAS! ALAS! FOR THIS SIN THE KURUS WILL BE DESTROYED.

A JUBILANT DURYODHANA TURNED TO PRATIKAMI, A SUTA.

GO, BRING DRAUPADI HERE.

PRATIKAMI VENTURED GINGERLY INTO DRAUPADI'S PRESENCE.

I HAVE COME TO TAKE YOU TO DURYODHANA. YOU HAVE BEEN STAKED AND LOST BY YUDHISHTHIRA.

A KING STAKING HIS WIFE, AWAY! ALAS HE WAS SURELY INTOXICATED WITH DICE.

DID HE HAVE NOTHING ELSE TO STAKE?

HE DIDN'T. HE STAKED AND LOST ALL, EVEN HIMSELF.

GO BACK AND FIND OUT WHOM HE LOST FIRST — HIMSELF OR ME? THEN COME TO TAKE ME.

WHEN PRATIKAMI CARRIED DRAUPADI'S QUERY TO DURYODHANA—

SHE SHALL GET HER ANSWERS HERE. GO, DUHSHASANA. BRING HER TO US.

DUHSHASANA BROKE INTO DRAUPADI'S CHAMBER.

CAST ASIDE YOUR MODESTY. COME, YOU HAVE BEEN WON BY US. ACCEPT THE KURUS AS YOUR LORDS.

DRAUPADI TRIED TO RUN AWAY BUT ROARING WITH ANGER DUHSHASANA RAN AFTER HER.

COME HERE, YOU SLAVE...

YUDHISHTHIRA IS BOUND BY THE RULES OF GAMBLING. HE IS BLAMELESS. BUT O WRETCH, MY OTHER HUSBANDS WILL NOT FORGIVE YOU.

AS DUHSHASANA DRAGGED DRAUPADI IN, NOT A WORD OF PROTEST ROSE FROM THE ASSEMBLY.

CHOOSE ANOTHER HUSBAND NOW WHO WILL NOT MAKE YOU A SLAVE BY GAMBLING.

THE KURU ELDERS HAVE LOST THEIR REASON. WHY ELSE DO THEY LOOK SILENTLY ON THIS GREAT CRIME?

WHILE CRYING THUS IN DISTRESS SHE CAST A GLANCE AT HER HELPLESS HUSBANDS.

YUDHISHTHIRA, LOOK AT HER GLANCES FULL OF MODESTY AND ANGER AND KNOW THAT YOUR ACT WAS A HIGHLY IMPROPER ONE.

AT THAT MOMENT—

THE VERY CLOTHES SHE IS WEARING BELONG TO US! SHE IS OUR SLAVE.

O KRISHNA, SAVE ME!

15

THEN LO! AS ONE GARMENT WAS REMOVED, ANOTHER MIRACULOUSLY COVERED HER.

FRUSTRATED AND ASHAMED DUHSHASANA SAT DOWN. BHEEMA, QUIVERING WITH ANGER, TOOK AN OATH.

I SHALL, IN THE BATTLEFIELD, TEAR OPEN THE BREAST OF THIS VILLAIN OF THE BHARATA RACE, AND DRINK HIS LIFE BLOOD.

THEN ALL THE ASSEMBLED KINGS CENSURED THE SONS OF DHRITHARASHTRA.

ALAS! THE KURUS HAVE NOT YET ANSWERED THE QUESTION PUT TO THEM.

DUHSHASANA TRIED TO DRAG DRAUPADI AWAY BUT SHE RESISTED.

O KURU ELDERS, I CANNOT BEAR THIS PERSECUTION, ANY LONGER. AM I WON OR NOT? I SHALL ABIDE BY YOUR VERDICT.

AS SHE WAITED FOR THE VERDICT, DURYODHANA BECAME BOLDER.

COME DRAUPADI, YOU ARE WON BY ME. COME SIT ON MY LAP.

MARK MY WORDS, DURYODHANA, I SHALL BREAK THAT THIGH IN BATTLE...

AT THAT MOMENT JACKALS HOWLED, ASSES BRAYED AND BIRDS OF PREY SHRIEKED. DHRITHARASHTRA WAS ALARMED BY THESE EVIL PORTENTS.

O CHASTE DRAUPADI, ASK FROM ME ANY BOON YOU DESIRE.

LET YUDHISHTHIRA BE FREED FROM SLAVERY. LET NOT POSTERITY SPEAK OF OUR SON AS BORN OF A SLAVE.

O VIRTUOUS GIRL, ASK FOR A SECOND BOON.

LET BHEEMA, ARJUNA, AND THE TWINS BE FREED FROM SLAVERY, TOO.

O DAUGHTER, ASK FOR A THIRD BOON.

I DO NOT COVET BOONS. MY HUSBANDS WILL ACHIEVE THE REST.

LATER WHEN YUDHISHTHIRA APPROACHED DHRITHARASHTRA TO TAKE LEAVE OF HIM—

TAKE YOUR WEALTH AND REIGN AT MY COMMAND. LET THERE BE BROTHERLY LOVE BETWEEN YOU AND YOUR COUSINS.

WHEN DURYODHANA LEARNT OF THIS HE WENT TO DHRITHARASHTRA.

O FATHER, THE PANDAVAS WILL NEVER FORGIVE THE INSULT TO DRAUPADI. WITH REGAL POWERS THEY WILL ANNIHILATE US. PERMIT US TO EXILE THEM BY ANOTHER GAME OF DICE.

THEN BRING BACK THE PANDAVAS. LET THERE BE ANOTHER GAME.

YUDHISHTHIRA WAS AWARE OF SHAKUNI'S DECEPTION, STILL HE CAME BACK TO THE DICE.

THE LOSERS MUST GO INTO EXILE TO THE FOREST FOR TWELVE YEARS, AND PASS THE THIRTEENTH YEAR IN SOME INHABITED PLACE — UNRECOGNISED. IF RECOGNISED THEY MUST RETURN TO AN EXILE OF ANOTHER TWELVE YEARS. ON THE EXPIRY OF THE THIRTEENTH YEAR THE LOSER WILL GET BACK HIS KINGDOM.

YUDHISHTHIRA AGREED AND SHAKUNI CAST THE DICE.

LOOK! I HAVE WON.

AS DRAUPADI AND THE PANDAVAS LEFT THE HALL—

O DRAUPADI, THE DARK FORESTS AND HUSBANDS IN RAGS ARE NOT FOR YOU. CHOOSE ONE AMONG US AND STAY HERE.

BUT DRAUPADI UTTERED NOT A WORD.

AFTER CONSOLING THEIR WEEPING MOTHER KUNTI, DRAUPADI AND THE PANDAVAS SET OUT FOR THE FOREST.

I VOW THAT THIRTEEN YEARS HENCE THE WIVES OF THOSE VILLAINS WILL LANGUISH IN DESOLATE WIDOWHOOD.

LORD SURYA BROUGHT A GIFT FOR THE VIRTUOUS PANDAVAS AS THEY ENTERED THE FOREST.

FOOD COOKED IN THIS VESSEL WILL BE INEXHAUSTIBLE AT EACH MEAL TILL DRAUPADI EATS.

KRISHNA DIVINING THE SAD PLIGHT OF THE PANDAVAS, CAME TO THEM. WHEN DRAUPADI SAW THE COMPASSIONATE ONE, SHE POURED OUT HER HEART TO HIM.

MY BIRTH WAS NOBLE AND UNIQUE. MY HUSBANDS ARE MIGHTY MEN. YOU ARE MY FRIEND. STILL I AM ABUSED THUS AND YOU WATCH IN SILENCE.

MOVED BY HER DISTRESS, KRISHNA TOOK AN OATH.

THE WIVES OF THOSE WHO HAVE INJURED YOU WILL SUFFER THIS AGONY. YOU SHALL YET REIGN AS THE QUEEN. MY WORDS SHALL NOT BE IN VAIN.

DEAR DRAUPADI, BE CONSOLED. YOUR HUMILIATIONS WILL BE AVENGED FOURTEEN YEARS FROM NOW.

BUT DRAUPADI'S RAGE SMOULDERED ON. ONE DAY IN THE FOREST—

DON'T ALL THESE INSULTS HEAPED ON US EVER MAKE YOU ANGRY? NOW IS THE TIME TO USE OUR MIGHT.

AT THAT MOMENT BHEEMA SIGHED IN WRATH.

DRAUPADI IS RIGHT. THE KAURAVAS MISTAKE YOUR MORALITY FOR COWARDICE. LET US WAGE A WAR FOR OUR KINGDOM.

DO NOT BE IMPETUOUS. IT WOULD BE AGAINST DHARMA, WHICH IS DIVINE AND SUPERIOR TO LIFE ITSELF. I AGREED TO THE STAKES THOUGH I KNEW SHAKUNI TO BE DISHONEST.

MANY WERE THE SAGES WHO VISITED THE PANDAVAS IN THE FOREST. DRAUPADI FED ALL OF THEM TAKING CARE TO BE THE LAST TO EAT.

THE HAPPINESS OF THE PANDAVAS IN EXILE ROUSED THE ENVY OF DURYODHANA. HE PLOTTED AGAINST THEM.

DURVASA THE ILL TEMPERED SAGE WILL SOON BE HERE. I COULD USE HIM.

DURVASA CAME AND WAS PLEASED WITH DURYODHANA'S LAVISH HOSPITALITY.

O KING, WHAT CAN I DO FOR YOU IN RETURN?

PLEASE GO WITH YOUR 10,000 DISCIPLES AND SEEK THE HOSPITALITY OF YUDHISHTHIRA, WHEN DRAUPADI HAS FINISHED EATING HER MEAL.

DURVASA AGREED AND ARRIVED AT THE FOREST.

WELCOME, O REVERED SAGE. COME BACK AFTER YOUR ABLUTIONS AND PRAYER AT THE RIVER YONDER.

WE WILL COME. LET DRAUPADI HAVE A GOOD MEAL READY FOR US.

DRAUPADI WAS AGHAST.

KRISHNA, YOU MUST SAVE ME FROM DURVASA'S WRATH.

KRISHNA, THE ALL-KNOWING, APPEARED.

DRAUPADI, I AM HUNGRY. LET ME EAT FIRST. THEN I WILL SEE WHAT I CAN DO.

DRAUPADI WAS MISERABLE.

I HAVE JUST TOLD YOU — THERE IS NO FOOD!

THIS IS NO TIME FOR JOKES; I AM TIRED AND HUNGRY. GO. FETCH THE VESSEL AND SHOW IT TO ME.

WHEN DRAUPADI BROUGHT THE VESSEL—

WHAT IS THIS? A PARTICLE OF RICE AND VEGETABLE STUCK HERE?

MAY THE SOUL OF THE UNIVERSE BE SATIATED WITH IT.

MEANWHILE AT THE RIVER—

NOT A SINGLE MORSEL FOR ME. NO!

I FEEL AS IF I'VE EATEN FOR SIX.

HOW CAN WE FACE DRAUPADI? LET US SLINK AWAY.

THUS DRAUPADI WITH KRISHNA'S HELP THWARTED DURYODHANA'S ATTEMPT TO HARASS THEM.

THE YEARS PASSED. AT LAST THE THIRTEENTH AND THE MOST DIFFICULT YEAR CAME ROUND.

WE SHALL SPEND THIS YEAR IN THE SERVICE OF KING VIRATA. I WILL GO AS KANKA, AN EXPERT IN DICE.

I WILL GO AS A COOK—BALLAVA.

WE WILL TEND HIS HORSES AND GRAZE HIS COWS.

I WILL GO AS A DANCE TEACHER.

I WILL GO AS SAIRANDHRI AND SEEK SERVICE AS QUEEN SUDHESHNA'S MAID.

SO IN THEIR RESPECTIVE GUISES DRAUPADI AND THE PANDAVAS SOUGHT AND SECURED SERVICE IN THE PALACE OF VIRATA.

TEN MONTHS HAD PASSED WHEN KEECHAKA, THE QUEEN'S BROTHER, WAS SMITTEN BY THE BEAUTY OF DRAUPADI.

WHO OWNS YOU?

I AM THE WIFE OF FIVE MIGHTY GANDHARVAS.

BUT THIS DID NOT DAMPEN KEECHAKA'S ARDOUR.

I AM A SLAVE TO YOUR BEAUTY. BE MY WIFE.

BEWARE! O SON OF A SUTA. I AM DEAR TO MY HUSBANDS. IF ENRAGED THEY WILL KILL YOU.

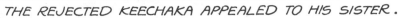

THE REJECTED KEECHAKA APPEALED TO HIS SISTER.

IT IS EITHER SAIRANDHRI OR DEATH, FOR ME. HATCH A PLOT, SUDHESHNA, TO SEND HER TO ME.

I SHALL TRY.

KEECHAKA LEFT AND SUDESHNA SENT FOR DRAUPADI.

GO TO KEECHAKA AND BRING ME SOME WINE. I AM THIRSTY.

DRAUPADI WAS ALARMED.

O QUEEN, HE IS SURE TO MOLEST ME.

SENT BY ME, HE WON'T DARE TO GO WITHOUT FEAR.

A TREMBLING DRAUPADI STOOD BEFORE KEECHAKA.

THE QUEEN HAS SENT ME TO YOU FOR SOME WINE.

O GENTLE ONE, LET OTHERS TAKE IT TO HER. YOU COME AND SIT NEAR ME...

DRAUPADI TURNED AND FLED.

OF WHAT USE IS THE PROWESS OF MY HUSBANDS WHEN THEY CANNOT PROTECT ME FROM SUCH INSULTS.

KEECHAKA CAUGHT UP WITH HER AND KICKED HER IN THE PRESENCE OF ALL. YUDHISHTHIRA AS KANKA WAS HELPLESS.

GO TO THE QUEEN, SAIRANDHRI. THE GANDHARVAS WILL LOOK AFTER YOU.

THIS SUFFERING SHOULD BE THEIRS. THE ELDEST OF THEM GAMBLING AWAY WHILE I PRACTISE PIETY!

THAT NIGHT DRAUPADI WENT TO BHEEMA.

BHEEMA! YOU SLEEP LIKE A DEAD ONE EVEN WHEN YOUR WIFE HAS BEEN INSULTED BY A CAD.

HUSH! PATIENCE, DEAR ONE. WE WILL SOON FREE YOU FROM GRIEF.

WITH YUDHISHTHIRA FOR A HUSBAND I WILL NEVER BE FREE OF GRIEF. THE INSULT AFTER THE GAME OF DICE STILL RANKLES IN ME.

MY PRINCESS, YOU HAVE ENDURED MUCH.

BUT EVEN I CANNOT ENDURE, WHEN MY WEAK HUSBANDS WATCH ME BEING KICKED BY A SUTA.

AT THAT MOMENT I WANTED TO RAZE THIS KINGDOM TO THE GROUND, BUT YUDHISHTHIRA FORBADE ME BY A GLANCE.

AM I TO BE SACRIFICED FOR THE SAKE OF THAT ADDICT TO DICE?

DRAUPADI, RENOUNCE YOUR WRATH. IF YUDHISHTHIRA HEARS SUCH REBUKES FROM YOU, HE WILL GIVE UP HIS LIFE.

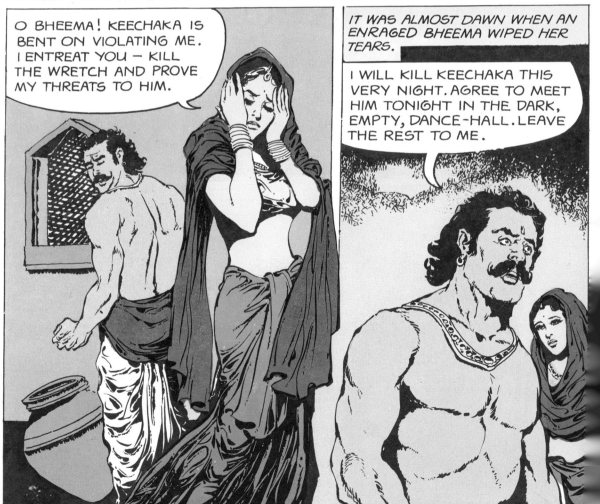

O BHEEMA! KEECHAKA IS BENT ON VIOLATING ME. I ENTREAT YOU — KILL THE WRETCH AND PROVE MY THREATS TO HIM.

IT WAS ALMOST DAWN WHEN AN ENRAGED BHEEMA WIPED HER TEARS.

I WILL KILL KEECHAKA THIS VERY NIGHT. AGREE TO MEET HIM TONIGHT IN THE DARK, EMPTY, DANCE-HALL. LEAVE THE REST TO ME.

DRAUPADI DID AS SHE WAS TOLD. BHEEMA LAY IN WAIT. THE MOMENT KEECHAKA ENTERED—

DRAUPADI WILL NOW KNOW PEACE.

THE FOURTEENTH YEAR CAME ROUND. BUT DURYODHANA REFUSED TO SURRENDER EVEN FIVE VILLAGES, LEAVE ALONE THE KINGDOM. WHILE THE PANDAVAS WERE PLANNING THEIR NEXT MOVE DRAUPADI TURNED TO KRISHNA.

SHAME ON THE SKILLED ARCHER ARJUNA AND SHAME ON THE MIGHTY BHEEMA THAT DURYODHANA IS STILL ALIVE.

THEN OVERCOME BY EMOTION SHE WEPT ALOUD.

O KRISHNA! THESE TRESSES WERE SEIZED BY DUHSHASANA. I WILL KNOW NO PEACE TILL HIS HANDS ARE RIPPED OFF.

THIRTEEN YEARS HAVE I WAITED KEEPING THE EMBERS OF REVENGE GLOWING IN MY HEART!

KRISHNA WAS QUICK TO ASSURE HER.

O DRAUPADI, YOU WILL SEE YOUR ENEMIES KILLED AND YOUR HUSBANDS REINSTATED.

WAR WAS DECLARED BETWEEN THE PANDAVAS AND THE KAURAVAS – A WAR THAT LASTED EIGHTEEN LONG DAYS. ON THE BATTLEFIELD, BHEEMA ATTACKED DUHSHASANA AND BROKE HIS LIMBS.

THIS FOR DRAGGING DRAUPADI BY THE HAIR AND ATTEMPTING TO DISROBE HER.

THEN BHEEMA FULFILLED THE TERRIBLE OATH HE HAD TAKEN THIRTEEN YEARS AGO.

I WILL SOON REDEEM MY OTHER PLEDGE BY BREAKING THE THIGH OF DURYODHANA.

THE BATTLE RAGED ON. WITH THE SKILFUL MANOEUVRING OF KRISHNA, THE VICTORY OF THE PANDAVAS BECAME A CERTAINTY.

AT LAST BHEEMA HAD THE OPPORTUNITY TO TAKE UP HIS MACE AGAINST DURYODHANA.

YUDHISHTHIRA MADE A MISTAKE IN STAKING THE VICTORY ON THIS DUEL.

BHEEMA AND DURYODHANA BOTH MIGHTY WARRIORS, FOUGHT LONG AND HARD.

IF BHEEMA DOES NOT KILL HIM SOON DURYODHANA WILL RETAIN THE KINGDOM.

AS INTENDED BHEEMA HEARD THIS. THE MEMORY OF THE GREAT OUTRAGE CAME VIVIDLY TO HIS MIND.

YOU DARED INSULT DRAUPADI IN THE ASSEMBLY BECAUSE I WAS HELPLESS.

HE LOOKED UP AND SAW KRISHNA SLAP HIS THIGH.

BHEEMA TOOK THE CUE.

TODAY WILL I BREAK THAT THIGH. TODAY WILL I FULFIL MY VOW.

THEN THE VICTORIOUS PANDAVAS BLEW THEIR CONCHES. BHEEMA'S OATHS HAD BEEN CARRIED OUT. KRISHNA'S PROMISE TO DRAUPADI WAS FULFILLED.

YUDHISHTHIRA BECAME THE EMPEROR AND DRAUPADI ONCE MORE THE CHERISHED QUEEN OF POWERFUL, VIRTUOUS KINGS.